**DISCLAIMER:**

No liability is assumed for the inform his e-book. All material is intend ly and is not intended to provide w to Get Over OCD should be u upon as the sole source of

Specific medical advic ed health-c

Always check with your doctor before beginning any new health regimen or trying something new.

# Why Did I Write This Book?

As you know, obsessive compulsive disorder is the kind of disorder that has the power to completely ruin a person's life. It nearly ruined mine. I lost many friends, missed out on many great opportunities and experiences. Over the years I have purchased many books on OCD. All of them had the same problems. They devoted a large part of the book to describing OCD. Why would a sufferer need to read what the disorder is like? No doctor can describe the disorder as well as a person who suffers from it. What I and every other sufferer need is a guide that will help get rid of OCD. These books did not have that at all. They had some good points but they were scattered and difficult to remember. There was no clear system that a person can apply to beat the disorder.

After much research I finally understood what it takes to get over OCD. It was amazing to feel like OCD is finally losing its power over me. After many years I finally feel like I got my life back. I finally feel in control. How could I not tell others about it? I know how difficult it is to have OCD. I need to tell others how to beat it. Please keep in mind that I am not a professional writer. I am not a doctor. I am just a person who knows how to beat OCD. I have beaten it and I know you can too.

# How to Identify an OCD Thought

As an OCD sufferer you know that OCD is a disorder composed of obsessions and compulsions. However sometimes it is very difficult to know when a "normal" thought ends and an OCD thought begins. During my battle with OCD I had a very hard time figuring out which thoughts were OCD thoughts and which were real life fears and concerns. This chapter will show you how to clearly identify OCD thoughts.

***IT IS AN OCD THOUGHT IF YOU GET A THOUGHT AND YOU QUESTION WHETHER OR NOT THE THOUGHT IS OCD. THIS MEANS THAT IT IS AN OCD THOUGHT. IF IT WASN'T OCD YOU WOULD NOT QUESTION IT.***

This is the rule. Here is a list of other ocd thought characteristics.

### OCD Thoughts Are Repetitive

When an OCD thought is created, the person often has a very hard time getting rid of it. It is almost like a song playing over and over again in the mind. Many times the sufferer understands OCD's faulty logic but the thought doesn't go away.

### OCD Thoughts Distractive

You can notice that whenever an OCD thought enters your brain your concentration drops significantly. It can suddenly become very difficult to focus on anything else other than your thought. The amount of time spent on thinking about the obsession can be hours and can actually take up most of the day. Even your real life problems can seem less important than the OCD thought.

### OCD Thoughts Are Unwanted

What I mean by that is that you do not like your thought. When you get it you want it to go away.

### The Thought Goes Against Your Core Beliefs

If you are a very sensitive and kind person, you may get thoughts that are violent and aggressive. If you love your significant other, it may make you doubt those feelings. It always goes against your real thoughts. This is what creates the anxiety. After all, if it went along with your real thoughts, it would not cause anxiety.

### OCD Thoughts Cause Anxiety

The amount of anxiety that is caused by the thoughts can vary from extreme to moderate, but anxiety is always present. The next two characteristics are not always present but you need to know them in case they do come up.

### OCD Thoughts Can Begin With "What If"

Have you ever had an OCD thought that "what if-ed" a worst case scenario? It goes something like this: A woman is leaving the house. She suddenly gets a thought; "What if I didn't turn off the oven and the house will burn down?"

### OCD Thoughts Can Follow Your Particular "Theme" of OCD

What I mean by that is that if, for example, your OCD is always about catching AIDS from touching doorknobs and you suddenly get a thought that you may have got AIDS when you touched a handle, then it is OCD. What helped me is to make a chart of all my OCD thoughts and keep adding to it every time a new one comes up. Also note what triggered the thought and the time it took to get over a thought. Note your level of anxiety (1-10). Here is an example of what it should look like:

1. OCD Thought

2. Thought Trigger Anxiety Level

3. Time To Get Over the Thought

Remember that themes often change so just because a thought doesn't follow your usual OCD theme there is no need to doubt it. It is important to note that when your OCD starts to improve you will get more thoughts but they will cause less anxiety and will change often. During recovery you may get as many as 10 different thoughts a day, whereas before you may have gotten only one or two that "stuck" all day. I believe this happens because the brain is so used to the constant state of high alert and anxiety, that it tries to give you more thoughts to return to a familiar level of high stress. After some time it will fade and the brain will get used to your new calmer state.

***REMEMBER, IF YOU ARE EVER IN DOUBT WHETHER THE THOUGHT IS OCD KNOW THAT THE VERY ACT OF DOUBTING YOUR THOUGHT MEANS IT IS AN OCD THOUGHT.***

# How to Get Over OCD
# Step 1 - Commitment

OCD is one of the most devastating mental disorders. It can turn one's life upside down. OCD has the power to ruin friendships, destroy marriages and cause job loss. Beating this disorder may be one of the biggest challenges in your life. You need to be mentally ready to fight back. It will be very difficult but if you follow this guide, you will overcome OCD.

### What You Need to Consider Before Starting This Program

It will take approximately 6 months to 1 year to significantly reduce your OCD. The length of time it takes to recover depends on the severity of your disorder. The longer each particular obsession "sticks around", the longer it will take to get over it. It also depends on your will power to keep fighting against OCD. The more effort you put in, the faster you will see the results.

Most people notice an improvement within the first month. You will notice that the obsessions are losing their hold on you, and you will begin to feel more in control. The actual number of obsessions you get may increase, but that doesn't mean anything. What you need to judge your improvement on is how you feel each day. If the obsessions are coming and going and causing less distress than normal, it means you are improving. You will feel it right away when you will start to get better. It really is not that hard to get rid of this condition when you have the right tools. You will need to take the time daily to achieve and maintain your progress. This is non-negotiable. You need to make this battle against OCD your top priority.

You will have days when your anxiety is extreme. You must not be afraid of having those days. Especially in the beginning it will get worse before it gets better. You must stay strong no matter how bad OCD gets. Remember that you are in this to win the war against OCD. Every time OCD presents a challenge you need to step up and show who is boss.

### Why This Step Is Important

This first step is not just an intro. It's a commitment to keep going, to not give up until you overcome this disorder. Every time you have a difficult day, remember the commitment you have made to stay with this program, and just keep going. It will get easier, I promise.

*REMEMBER THAT YOUR WELL BEING IS THE NUMBER ONE PRORITY IN YOUR LIFE. ALL YOUR OTHER COMMITMENTS MUST COME SECOND BECAUSE IF YOU DON'T FEEL WELL YOU WILL NOT BE ABLE TO TAKE CARE OF ANYTHING ELSE.*

*YOU MUST ALWAYS COME FIRST.*

# Five Step Guide to Getting Over OCD
## Step 2 - Learn To Trust Yourself.

OCD is a disorder of doubt. Every time an obsessive thought enters your mind you are presented with a choice to either believe the thought or not. What you choose is extremely important for your recovery. This chapter will explain why you must not listen to your obsessive thoughts and will show you the correct ways to disable them.

### Stop Buying Into the Thoughts

Every time you choose to believe an obsessive thought you are training your brain that the OCD thoughts are valid. You say to your brain that you are choosing to trust the OCD thoughts and not yourself. By now you probably had thousands of those thoughts which mean you have been repeatedly training your brain to trust OCD thoughts and accept them as true.

The actual subject of these thoughts does not matter. They are not real. What matters is that after repetitive training, your brain will automatically accept them as real.

Since when a thought pops into your head it seems very important, you are also training your brain to take these thoughts very seriously. That's why many times an OCD thought may seem disabling when it first enters your mind. In order to get over OCD you need to retrain your brain on how it deals with these types of thoughts. Just like it learns to automatically accept them as real, it can learn to automatically accept them as false and unimportant. In time it will dismiss them before you even notice these thoughts.

## How to Make Your Brain Disregard OCD
## Thoughts Automatically

It is very simple. You need to trust yourself. You need to show your mind that these thoughts are irrelevant. To do that, you have to choose to view them as irrelevant. Every time you have a thought that seems like an OCD thought, choose to view it as irrelevant. No matter how real the thought seems you need to immediately write it off as false. The faster you dismiss the thought the quicker you will forget about it.

### Here Is What Your New Thought Process Should Be:

-OH MY GOD! I just thought that what if...

-I don't care. I trust myself. It is just a thought and I am not going to alter my life in any way because of this thought.

- I am not going to participate in thinking about it. If the thought comes into my mind on its own I will view it as an outside observer, with as little emotion

and involvement as possible.

-but what if this thought is real?

-it is not real. I trust myself and I trust that this thought is false. I am not going to spend any more time going over it. In fact I am so sure that the thought is false, that I don't care if it stays in my mind or not. It can be there forever, I don't care because it is not real.

Once you make the choice to trust yourself you can't go back on that choice. Every time the thought repeats itself you have to disregard it. Accept it as one of the thoughts, but view it as an irrelevant one. It should not matter whether this thought is there or not. Why would it matter if it offers no real input?

Think of your thought as a bird chirping in the sky. You can't do anything about it because it is out of your reach. You don't care what it's saying because it has no meaning to you. All you can do is accept its presence and move on with your life. To say that you trust yourself is a huge step towards recovery. Even if you do not fully believe that, it shows that you no longer trust the OCD thought.

***REMEMBER, EVERY TIME YOU HAVE AN OCD THOUGHT, SAY TO YOURSELF: "I TRUST MYSELF" SAY IT AND CONTINUE GOING ABOUT YOUR LIFE AS IF THE THOUGHT IS NOT THERE. IF YOU DO THIS THE THOUGHT WILL LEAVE ON ITS OWN. AFTER ALL, THE ONLY THING THAT IS GIVING IT POWER IS YOUR BELIEF IN THE THOUGHT.***

You alone have the power to either increase the importance of the thought or diminish it. When you have full trust in yourself the thought will not stick to you. It will come into your mind, show itself and then fade away. It will have no choice but to fade away, since you will no longer believe it. You may not actually believe what you are saying at first. Don't worry. Just go through the motions and try to believe it as much as you can. If you practice this thought process, your brain will start to adjust and your anxiety will subside.

# Step 3 - Stop Avoiding!

Have you ever made a choice to not do something because of your OCD? Something that you really wanted to do, but chose not to because you knew it would trigger your OCD? Avoidance is extremely common in this disorder. It is common because every OCD sufferer wants the same thing – to not have to face OCD. They think that the simplest way to stop OCD is to avoid situations that cause OCD. This is very wrong. This chapter will explain to you why you should never avoid situations that trigger your OCD.

### Why You Shouldn't Avoid

There is a part of your brain called Amygdala. It responsible for the anxiety you feel. Since this part of the brain is reactionary, you can't reason with it. It only understands your actions and reactions. You react to the situation with fear and avoid it. Your brain then makes sure that the next time when this type of situation arises to send you more anxiety, since this is now considered a situation you should be afraid of. It is basically repeating your reaction. You react with fear, and next time the fear will come to you and it will be intense. If you continue to avoid this particular situation, then other similar situations will start to feel scary and you will feel the need to avoid those too. This is how OCD progresses and gets worse. This is probably how your disorder got to where it is today.

Also, every time you make that choice you are telling your brain that you are not in control. You are letting your OCD choose for you and the more times it chooses the stronger it will become.

Try to remember the last time you avoided something. How did you feel when you made the choice to avoid? You probably felt like you were protecting yourself. You felt in control. Those feelings made you think that avoidance is a way to solve your OCD problems. What really happened is you missed out on something because you were afraid. You were afraid of something that was not real. Next time a similar situation arises it will be harder to face because you already sent a signal of fear to your brain.

You need to face all the situations you have been scared to face. I know that this is extremely difficult. This will take at least a few months to achieve. Just remember that any time you feel like you have to avoid something because of your OCD, make the choice and face it.

### Stop Avoiding Now!

Have you been invited to an event? Then go there. Are you scared to touch doorknobs? Make the choice to touch it. Are you afraid of bacteria? Go ahead and eat WITHOUT washing your hands. After all millions of people do these things and are still okay.

### What Happens When You First Stop Avoiding

When you first stop avoiding, it will feel like your OCD is getting worse. That is not actually true. You will feel worse because your brain has been used to avoiding for so long. It is used to having OCD dictate everything. Now you are in control. This type of change at first can be very difficult. During this time you will probably feel very anxious and will likely feel like quitting the whole program. The important thing is to stick it out. Just live through it and don't avoid anything. It will get better very quickly. For me the tough period lasted about two weeks. During this time my anxiety got really bad. At first I could barely function, but after that my anxiety started disappearing.

## Why It Is Important

Avoiding Avoidance is vital to your progress. This is the only way you can prove to your brain that you are the one in control. Say to yourself: "Go ahead OCD; give me all you've got. I am not going to hide from you anymore. I am not going to be scared anymore." By taking this aggressive approach to OCD, you will have a much quicker recovery than if you would have waited for OCD to come to you.

*IN ANY SITUATION, ASK YOURSELF; "WHAT MESSAGE AM I SENDING TO MY BRAIN RIGHT NOW?"*

*IF YOU ARE SENDING A MESSAGE OF FEAR AND DOUBT, OCD WINS.*

*IF YOU SEND THE MESSAGE OF STRENGTH AND INDIFFERENCE, THEN YOU WIN.*

*THE MORE TIMES YOU WIN, THE FASTER YOU WILL RECOVER. THIS IS THE BASIC PRINCIPLE OF OVERCOMING OCD.*

So remember, every time you are faced with a situation that can trigger your OCD, use it as an opportunity to face your fears.

# Step 4 - Stop Seeking Reassurance

Another big part of OCD is the constant need for reassurance. When the sufferer gets a new OCD thought, his immediate reaction is doubt. What if…. After doubt comes the panic and fear. At this point the only thing that the sufferer wants to do is to get rid of this fear. This is the point where reassurance comes in.

## Types of Reassurance

There are two different ways to seek that reassurance. It is important to be able to clearly identify them, so next time you feel the urge to ask for reassurance you can avoid it. This is one thing in OCD that you should avoid.

## Type 1

The first type is reassurance that comes from people around the sufferer. The sufferer would ask someone else if the thought he is having is valid. The person answering him will explain that the thought is not valid. After this answer the sufferer will feel better for a short while, and then will feel the need to ask again. Maybe he will find some detail he forgot to mention, or he thought up a new way his fear may be true. No matter what the reasoning is, the need to ask for reassurance again will arise. This loop of seeking more and more reassurance can last for a long time. Every time the sufferer is fooled into believing he will have permanent relief from his fear. However the relief only lasts a short time and a need to seek more reassurance arises again, and again, and again.

## Type 2

The second type of reassurance does not require anyone else's help. The sufferer checks by himself, to make sure the problem is not real. This can be done through the internet search or by reading encyclopedias and other books on the subject that the patient fears. This type of checking causes even more confusion because the information the sufferer finds online may be inaccurate and may not match up with information from books or other sources.

It is very important to know that both of these types have almost the same effect. They make your OCD worse.

How? Well, just like avoidance, it shows your brain that you are taking this situation seriously. Why else would you go out of your way to check or ask someone? You are basically saying to your brain that the obsessive thought is real. How do you expect your brain to react? Obviously, by sending you more fear and doubt.

Reassurance seems like a way to quickly solve the situation. However, instead of solving it, it gets you deeper in. This is how it works:

When you seek reassurance your brain also receives the signal of panic about a particular situation. So, to make sure the situation is not going to cause harm, it automatically checks for all the loopholes in your obsession. Here is what I mean:

You obsess that you may have touched a door handle and now you have aids. So you seek reassurance by getting an HIV test. It is negative. Now the brain starts checking for loopholes. What if that test was inaccurate? What if it didn't detect it by mistake? So you seek more reassurance by getting another test. This kind of obsessive chain can continue endlessly. The only way out is to stop seeking all reassurance. Refer to chapter one about trusting yourself. Exercise this type of unconditional trust against all your what ifs. This is very difficult to do but unfortunately it is the only way out. There is no other way.

Until you cut out all reassurance you will not get better. Also the speed with which you get better directly relates to the amount of reassurance you seek.

Because reassurance evolves other people, you need to let them know that they should not give you reassurance. Explain to them how reassurance can stop your progress and that by not reassuring you, they are actually helping you. Personally, I started out asking for a lot of reassurance. It took almost a year to completely stop. At first I just made a decision to ask for reassurance once for every obsession, and then slowly progressed to not at all. You have to remember that the process of getting better is not linear, but rather bumpy. Sometimes you will be able to stand strong and not ask and sometimes you may cave in. As long as there is progress, it's okay.

So now that you have all the information you need, how do you proceed?

Any time you get an urge to seek reassurance you need to stop yourself from doing that. This takes a lot of courage, self-trust and will power. It seems almost impossible at first but it will get easier. Your brain will start getting used to enduring the anxiety without seeking reassurance. The act of asking for reassurance is the act of resistance. Every time you resist you make your OCD worse. You give it power. Just like every time you avoid.

These two actions are similar because they are driven by fear. These fears are not valid. They need to be disregarded. Say to yourself: "I know that this thought is just an OCD thought. I trust myself and I will not ask or otherwise seek unneeded reassurance. There is no real problem. The only problem I have is my OCD. To get over it I need to stop seeking reassurance." By saying this to yourself you are clearly identifying the reasons why you are choosing to not seek reassurance. You also remind your brain that you trust yourself. This mindset is the key to getting over OCD. Treat every single OCD as practice of not seeking reassurance. After a few tries it will not seem like such a big deal. It will become the new way you deal with OCD.

# Step 5 – Stop the Guilt.

This chapter may not be for everyone. Not every person who has OCD experiences feelings of guilt, but many do, so I need to talk about it.

OCD guilt comes from the fact that the sufferer is so ashamed of his obsessions that he feels guilty.

## Where does the guilt come from?

You may feel guilty for having bad thoughts. The very act of feeling guilt means that these thoughts are going against your core beliefs and principals. This means you are a good person and you have nothing to feel guilty about.

These thoughts are a part of your disorder. They are in your brain but they are not yours. You need to understand that these thought do not define who you are. Your actions do. You have not done anything wrong and do not let OCD convince you otherwise.

Here is an example:

A person who thinks that he has aids feels guilty when he is having intercourse with his girlfriend. He has been previously tested and it was negative. He is still not convinced and his obsession is actually making him feel guilty because he thinks he will pass the virus to his girlfriend. By giving in to feelings of guilt, he is also giving in to the thought that he may have aids.

As we discussed in previous chapters, this submissive behavior makes your brain think that the thought is actually true and valid.

When the brain thinks that, it will act as if the thought was valid. In this case, by sending the sufferer more anxiety and guilt.

What is he doing wrong? He is allowing his OCD to alter his life by making it difficult for himself to have intercourse with his girlfriend. By altering his life based on OCD thoughts he is making them valid and making them "stick" in his brain.

He should instead acknowledge the thought and say to himself that he trusts himself, that he is a good person and that he has nothing to feel guilty about. He needs to live his life as if the thought is not there. Just ignoring it. If he does this, soon the thought will not be there.

So how do you fight against guilt? Start recognizing these feelings of guilt as part of your OCD thoughts. Say to yourself:

"These feelings of guilt are unnecessary. I am a good person. I trust myself. I have nothing to feel guilty about. I am just having these feelings because I have OCD. I don't care if these feelings are there or not, I will not react to them or take them seriously. Instead I will ignore them."

When you start to feel guilty the best thing to do is to acknowledge where the guilt is coming from and allow it stay there. Do not wish for it to go away. Just picture it like a dark cloud in a bright blue sky. Yes, it sticks out and is annoying but ultimately you don't care whether it is there or not. It makes no difference to you. All you can do is watch it. When you approach it that way, you put yourself in control. You show your brain that it is you who makes the choices about how you feel, and not your disorder.

After some repetition your brain will naturally let you make those choices without even engaging your OCD.

# Step 6 - Don't Give In to the Fear.

Fear is a big part of OCD. It is what fuels it. Without a fearful reaction your obsessions have no power over you. The only way that OCD can control you and keep you focused on an obsession is by scaring you with the fearful consequences. You need to remember that there is no need to fear the consequences, because the original thought is not real. If the obsession is not real then the feared consequences of that obsession are irrelevant. Why would you fear something that is irrelevant?

Another important point to remember is that when you give in to the feelings of fear, you send a signal to your brain that this particular situation is something to fear. The brain responds by trying to protect you from this particular situation. It does this by giving you the urge to avoid the situation. You have already read about avoidance in a previous chapter.

Here is an example:

A woman has an obsessive thought that if she does not clean something thoroughly her children can get sick and die. No matter how much she cleans, she can't get over the thought. The fear of her children getting sick is what is driving her to follow this thought.

She needs to say to herself:

*"This is just an OCD thought. It is not valid. There is no danger. I am ok with having this thought, but I will not respond to it with fear. I trust myself and I trust that I washed this enough for it to be clean. "*

Being ok with the thought is important. She dislikes the content of the thought but she can't control whether the thought is there or not. Since she can't control it all she can do is accept the existence of the thought. Since the thought is disliked and goes against her wishes and morals, it will leave on its own. The only thing keeping it there was her fearful reaction.

*BY TAKING THE FEARS SERIOUSLY YOU ARE FUELING YOUR OCD. STOP GIVING YOUR OCD THE GAS IT NEEDS TO RUN AND THE FEARS WILL STOP.*

All people get these types of thoughts. The reason why they stick with the people who have OCD, is that those people take these thoughts as important. Others just disregard them as meaningless.

Let's get back to the example. To get over her obsession the lady in the story needs to stop washing. This requires a lot of will power, but this is what needs to be done.

This response is what you should be doing every time OCD sends you fear. At first it will be very difficult but every time you practice this, it will get easier. After some time this response will become second nature to you. When this happens the brain will stop sending you more fear and you will be free of OCD.

# Daily Guide to Overcoming OCD

For me, whenever I read a book about OCD, it was always difficult to put into practice everything I learned. The ideas were good, but they have never provided a step by step guide to beating OCD. Without a guide you are basically left in the same place as when you started, you don't know what you should do next. So in this book I am going to provide a guide that you can follow each day to get rid of your obsessions. This will help you put into practice all the points discussed in the book.

There are three parts to the daily guide.

In Part 1 we will go over what your daily mindset should be and what you should do whenever you get a thought. I will tell you in detail how to stop and OCD thought before it gets very intense.

Part 2 is about the do's and don'ts of OCD. How to avoid common mistakes. It will also show you how to progress faster.

Part 3 is an emergency guide for when you are having a very difficult day and you feel like your obsessions have completely taken over. This part is extremely important because now you will have somewhere to turn to when nothing seems to work and you are feeling frustrated.

This daily guide should be followed as closely as possible, because the points made here is what is going to help you achieve recovery. If you follow it every day you will notice an immediate difference in your OCD.

# Daily Guide to Overcoming OCD

# Part 1 – Your New Daily Mindset

So you wake up in the morning and your first thought is an obsession. First of all, this is completely normal. The fact that OCD feels worse in the mornings has to do with the fact that serotonin levels are actually at their lowest in the mornings. I don't want to explain the scientific parts of it in detail, as it is not important. What is important is that you now have a distressing thought that you don't know how to deal with. What should you do next?

The first thing you should do is get back the control of your breathing. Breathe normally and don't allow your breathing pattern to speed up. While you do this make yourself smile. Yes, I know that smiling is the last thing you feel like right now, but you must smile. When you smile, you send a signal to your brain saying that you are happy. Do not make a tense smile. Just a small smile that not only shows on the face but also projects inwardly like an inner smile. Try it. I promise you will feel immediately better.

Do not stay in bed. When the thought comes you may often feel like you have no energy to deal with anything else. You want to stay in bed and be miserable. This kind of thought sends a signal to the brain that the obsession is important and because it is important, it must be valid. Do not send this signal.

Instead say to yourself:

***"OCD is sending me an obsessive thought, however it is not real or important and it will not have any effect on how I live my life. Not now, not today, not ever. I trust myself."***

When you say this to yourself you may feel immediate doubt over whether or not the thought is actually an OCD thought. That's because it is much easier to not be afraid of the thought if you knew for sure it was not real.

Remember the rule from a previous chapter: If you ever wonder if a thought is an OCD thought you must immediately accept it as an OCD thought. Don't let this doubt seep in any deeper. Accept it as OCD and get back to whatever it is you were doing. Take the time to say all this to yourself.

Remember what your responsibilities are today. What do you need to accomplish? If you feel like you may forget it later, write it down. Start doing whatever you need to do. Just go about your day like you don't have OCD. Every time you remember the thought do not try to get rid of it. Allow it to be in your brain. This sends your brain the signal that the thought is so unimportant that you don't even care whether it is there or not. This type signal is what will heal your OCD. As you go about your day you may face some situations that have the potential to trigger your OCD. When you have this type of challenge present itself, the first response is to avoid it all together. You may even have an excuse ready for why you are avoiding it. Maybe you are not ready, maybe you are too busy. This is a key moment. If at this moment you chose to avoid the "challenge", your brain will get a signal that you are afraid. That OCD is the one in control. This is why you must never avoid these types of situations.

Here is an example:

The sufferer is afraid of catching a virus such as AIDS. His work is giving blood bank donations and most people are participating. The sufferer immediately makes a connection between giving blood and getting AIDS. He is panicking. He has two choices. He can either make an excuse and stay scared or face his fear. If he chooses to face this fear, next time he has to give blood or participate in other activities with others. That is because the brain gets the signal that the sufferer is ok with facing it, so if this is ok, then other similar activities must be ok too. After all, the sufferer is now the one in control. If he chooses to avoid this activity, next time he has to do anything similar or even something slightly less anxiety provoking, he will get an OCD thought. The brain will produce it automatically to warn the sufferer against danger. The danger that the brain assumes the sufferer was facing. After all, the signal of fear and danger was sent to the brain when the choice was made to avoid the "scary" situation.

I hope you now understand how important it is to face all the life situations life gives you. Never be scared to face a challenge.

So another question that might arise is how do you keep calm while facing a challenge?

There have been many times when I was so overwhelmed with anxiety that it was difficult for me to remember anything I have learned about OCD. I was in complete panic mode. How was I to remember all the info without a clear step by step guide? This became frustrating for me and I knew that I needed an easy way to remember the system that I can use every time I get a thought. So I came up with a five step routine to stop an OCD thought.

# How to Stop an OCD Thought

**Step 1** - Normalize you breathing. Smile. If in public, smile on the inside.

**Step 2** - Attribute all unwanted and repetitive thoughts to OCD. Disregard them as false and therefore irrelevant. Say to yourself:

*I know that I am a good person.*

*I trust myself. I trust that this thought is an OCD thought.*

*I choose not to give into the fear and anxiety that this thought is sending me.*

*I CHOOSE not to react to it because it is not real.*

*I will not react with real emotion to thoughts that are not real. I don't care if the thought remains in my brain because it is irrelevant to me.*

*I will not give importance to the thought by wanting it to leave. It can stay as long as it wants. I simply don't care.*

**Step 3** - Do not ask for reassurance and do not avoid.

**Step 4** - Do not wish for your thoughts to go away. Allow them to stay in your mind.

**Step 5** - Carry on with your activity as if you did not have these thoughts. If the thought presents itself again, follow these steps again.

Remember, these steps must be done without giving in to the fear OCD sends. Acknowledge the fear signal but do not feed into it. Look at it as an observer.

# Daily Guide to Overcoming OCD – Part 2

## Do's and Don'ts of OCD

**Do** go outside as much as possible. Sunshine has a big effect on mental well-being. Make going outside every day your priority.

**Don't** let your OCD rule your life. Do what you want to do, not what OCD wants you to do.

**Do** start eating better. If you eat better, you will feel better.

**Don't** seek reassurance. This is very important.

**Do** let others know about your condition. Most people are much more understanding than you think.

**Don't** avoid anything because of your OCD. It's your life and you decide what you want to do with it.

**Do** spend time with friends and loved ones. It may be difficult at first but it will get easier.

# How to Speed Up Your Recovery

## Is This Technique For You?

This is an advanced technique to beating OCD. If you are just
starting out it may be too much for you to handle. If it is, that's ok,
just follow the method I described in the previous chapter and you
will get over your OCD. If you feel like you have got a good
handle on the technique described in the previous chapter and you
would like a challenge, then this chapter is for you.

## How It Works

Each time you get an OCD thought you can either choose to face it
or be scared by it. We already went over this. Well there is more
you can do. Instead of waiting for the thought to come to you, try
to force it out. This is done by finding situations that may trigger
your OCD. For example, if your OCD tells you that you need to
wash your hands purposely leave them dirty. Think of it as training
your OCD muscles. The more times you face all the situations that
scare you the less scared you will be.

For example a person who is terrified of dirt will purposely not
clean a certain area of the house. If a person is scared to be around
people he should have friends over to the house, slowly working
up to hosting a party. Instead of letting OCD come to you and
surprise you with a new thought you call it out on its false logic.
Your actions should say "I know this situation is normal for other
people and therefore it is normal for me too. I am not scared of
these thoughts and I can actually provoke them by participating in
this activity, event, etc.

## Why It Works

This technique speeds up the progress because it shows your brain
that you are the one actively in control and not OCD. There is a
big difference between this technique and the one we commonly
use. The difference is that here the patient is actively in control

and decides what he does. It shows to the brain that the person knows that he is a good person and that the person has trust in himself.

In the other technique the patient shows the same thing but in a passive way because the patient waits for OCD to come and get him. This shows slight mistrust in himself because he is still scared to be in situations that will cause OCD. To use this method you have to first eliminate all the avoidance which is a very difficult step. This why you can only do this step when you are already very far along in your recovery.

*EVERY TIME YOU CHOOSE TO FACE A SITUATION THAT TRIGGERS OCD,*
*YOU ARE TELLING OCD THAT YOU ARE THE BOSS.*
*YOU ARE RESPONSIBLE AND IN CONTROL OF YOUR ACTIONS.*
*YOU TRUST YOURSELF.*

This technique is based on the trust you have in yourself. When self trust is coupled with this technique there is no chance that OCD will win. You may feel slightly anxious afterwards, but you are gaining major points by facing your OCD.

# Daily Guide to Overcoming OCD – Part 3
# What to Do When OCD Gets Bad.

### Understand Why You Are Feeling Bad

How did it get out of control?

Did you avoid something? Did you seek reassurance from others?

Did you seek reassurance within yourself by maybe trying to think back to the situation?

Did you let fear take over, instead of ignoring the thought and writing it off as unreal and false?

Did you take the thought seriously and didn't attribute it to OCD immediately?

All these things make OCD thoughts cause more anxiety and stick around longer. By understanding what you did wrong you will be better equipped to not make the same mistakes next time. Also this understanding automatically makes you attribute this thought to OCD. You are being in control. So go ahead, explain to yourself why your OCD thought didn't come and go but became very intense instead.

### Spend Time Outdoors

Sunshine is very important. Especially if it is winter and there is less daylight. Make sure that when you feel your worst you spend at least 30 minutes to 1 hour a day outdoors. Get in touch with nature. It will help you. Don't forget to smile. Smiling sends a signal to your brain that everything is fine.

## What You Can Do Now To Get Rid of the Thought

1. Do not wish for it to leave. By wishing for it to leave you are showing OCD that you are scared of the thought. The thought is no real, so there is nothing to be scared of. If you are not scared of it why do you care if it's there or not?

2. Do not seek any reassurance of any kind on the thought.

3. Do not avoid any normal daily activities because of the thought.

4. Do not concentrate on the thought. Concentrate on other things. If you have trouble doing so make a list of what you need to do and do them one by one. This will occupy your attention which will put OCD in its place.

5. Allow your mind to do whatever it wants. You can't control it anyways so don't react to it at all. Just live your life as if nothing is happening.

Remember that this is not your first time dealing with anxiety. You will not feel this forever. If you follow these steps, each new day will be better than the last. All you have to do is follow the steps.

# How to Help a Relative with OCD

This last chapter is for parents, friends and partners of people who suffer from OCD. As an OCD sufferer I realize how difficult it can be to deal with someone who has OCD. You will need to be extremely strong if you want to help them.

So here are the things that you can do right now:

1. Stop giving them reassurance. If they repeatedly ask you same thing over and over again you need to calmly tell the person; "I have already answered this once. You are seeking reassurance because of your OCD. I care about you and I know that reassurance seeking is bad for your disorder. To help you recover I am not going to reassure you anymore."

2. Stop following their avoidance. If this person ask you to participate in an OCD ritual such as doing things to prevent their feared situation from happening you must say no. Here is an example: A person with OCD may ask their family members to wash their hands more than needed to avoid getting a feared illness. The person may demand that certain places or people be avoided because of OCD fears.

You cannot follow their OCD no matter how much they ask you. You must stay strong. In order for them to get better they need to face their fear and realize that there is nothing behind it. It is just an irrational fear.

Talk to them calmly and kindly. Make them feel loved and safe. If you feel frustrated take some time to calm down. Going into this type of conversation angry will not help you project kindness and love towards your loved one.

Here is what you should say:

**"*I understand that you want me to follow what OCD dictates, but I am not going to do that because it is detrimental to your progress. I care about you and want you to recover from OCD.***

***This is why I can no longer participate in these rituals.*"**

Most of the time people with OCD feel unloved and alone. They feel like no one understands them and no one really cares enough to understand. Since OCD thoughts can be very disturbing the sufferers often choose to keep everything inside and suffer in silence.

Please understand that your loved one is suffering greatly. He or she is not trying to make your life difficult. By the time most sufferers seek help they are spending most of the day plagued by OCD. It is very important that you get across to them how much you care about them.

Explain to them that you love and care for them. That you are going to do what it takes to help them. Understand that no matter what, it is always up to the sufferer to choose to fight OCD. All you can do is support them and cheer them on in their fight against OCD.

# In Conclusion

I want to take this time to thank you for purchasing this book. I am confident that if you use the advice given here, you will get over OCD forever.

Remember that no matter how real and scary the thoughts seem to be, they are only OCD thoughts. They are not real and the threat that they present is also false.

Do not let them scare you. Ignore them. Live your life as if these thoughts were not bothering you.

You just have to put your mind to it and make getting over OCD your number one priority.

Remember, every day that you follow this program your OCD will get weaker and weaker and eventually you will completely get over OCD.

Ali Greymond

Printed in Great Britain
by Amazon

70550432R00020